MW00637136

The Official Extreme Ownership Companion Workbook
Published under Jocko Publishing

US Edition Manufactured in the United States of America

www.jockopublishing.com
www.echelonfront.com

Library of Congress cataloging-in-publications data
The Official Extreme Ownership Companion Workbook

Library of Congress Registration

ISBN: 978-0981618876

Facilitated by: Jocko Publishing and Echelon Front

First Paperback Edition

9 10 8 7 6 5 4 3 2 1

1. Business
2. Self Help Techniques

OFFICIAL COMPANION WORKBOOK

EXTREME OWNERSHIP

LEARN. LEAD. WIN.

JOCKO WILLINK AND LEIF BABIN

WHATEVER CHALLENGES YOU MAY FACE...

LEADERSHIP IS THE SOLUTION.

THERE is no single inoculation to establish good leadership, for the individual or within an organization. You can't read one book, attend one seminar, or listen to just one lecture and suddenly be ready for any leadership challenge. Striving to become a good leader or to build good leadership inside of an organization is a campaign—a continual process that never stops. Like any skill, leadership takes practice. The more practice is put into leadership, the better the results and the better the leadership capability. Leadership can be practiced by reading about leadership principles, discussing leadership scenarios, role-playing, reviewing case studies, and a variety of other methods.

This workbook is not meant to replace the book, *Extreme Ownership: How U.S. Navy SEALs Lead and Win*, but as a complementary resource that takes the principles from that book and provides a platform for review, interaction, and discussion, which will drive a deeper understanding of the principles for individuals and an increased alignment around the concepts inside organizations.

The workbook not only follows the same path as Extreme Ownership, but also aligns with our online training platform, The Extreme Ownership ACADEMY (academy.echelon-front.com), allowing leaders and teams to learn information from a variety of angles and through different media platforms.

While there is no stringent methodology on how to utilize the workbook, it was structured to be as simple and straightforward as possible: the recommended path is to start at the beginning, review the principles of leadership in each section, and then utilize the questions and discussion points to expand comprehension and connect the principles to the actual leadership scenarios you face.

Remember that there isn't always a clear answer to your problems—leadership is not a scientific formula. Inherent in leadership are human beings, each with their own personalities, idiosyncrasies, opinions, egos, and agendas. It doesn't take only one standard process to lead. It takes skills. It takes practice. It takes knowledge and patience and compromise and perseverance. But the more you know and the better you understand leadership, the better leader you will be. That is what this book is for. Now...

LEARN, LEAD, WIN.

TABLE OF CONTENTS

INTRODUCTION
THE BATTLE OF RAMADI

THE bulk of our combat leadership lessons were learned in the Battle of Ramadi in 2006. Our SEAL unit, Task Unit Bruiser, fought alongside U.S. Soldiers, Marines, and Iraqi Soldiers in order to take back the city of Ramadi from enemy forces, provide security for the civilian populace, and ultimately lower the level of violence.

When Task Unit Bruiser arrived in April 2006, Ramadi, then a city of 400,000, was a violent terrorist stronghold and the epicenter of the Iraqi insurgency. U.S. forces only controlled about one third of the city. An insurgency of several thousand determined, well-armed enemy fighters controlled the rest. A U.S. intelligence report leaked to the press labeled Ramadi and the entire province of Al Anbar "all but lost." Very few thought the fight was winnable.

Our SEALs in Task Unit Bruiser worked closely alongside U.S. Marines of Air Naval Gunfire Liaison Company (ANGLICO) SALT 6. They often served as the first U.S. elements on the ground in the most dangerous, enemy-held neighborhoods in support of the main effort. This effort was led by brave U.S. Army and Marine units under the U.S. Army's "Ready First" Brigade Combat Team of the 1st Armored Division as they moved in to build combat outposts right in the enemy's backyard.

As American Soldiers and Marines, accompanied by Iraqi Soldiers, moved through the streets, they were covered by Task Unit Bruiser SEAL sniper overwatch elements, who were in turn covered by Marine Corps air assets overhead. Task Unit Bruiser disrupted enemy attacks and protected Army combat engineers who built and fortified combat outposts in enemy territory, and also provided protection for Soldiers and Marines who lived and patrolled out of those combat outposts.

While the fight for Ramadi was dynamic and complex, we focused on a simple task taken straight from the counterinsurgency manual: Secure the local populace by disrupting enemy operations, and building relationships with the local people. Each SEAL, Soldier, and Marine understood the mission and how every action they took on the battlefield contributed to achieving the objective.

Although the battlefield was daunting with a vast array of missions required, we prioritized our efforts to support the Ready First Brigade's "Seize, Clear, Hold, and Build" strategy as they executed the most effective way to impact the strategic mission. The Army understood that to gain the support of the people of Ramadi, American and Iraqi Soldiers had to live and operate within the city. This required establishing permanent Combat Outposts (COPS) in enemy territory, which was accomplished by a methodology called 'seize, clear, hold, and build.' The steps of that method were straightforward. 'Seize' meant to get control of some buildings in an enemy controlled area. 'Clear' meant removing enemy personnel from the area. 'Hold' meant remaining in the buildings that had been cleared. And finally, 'build' meant to first reinforce the buildings to withstand an enemy attack and then build the infrastructure and community in that neighborhood.

To support this effort, we had to split our forces into different independent elements. Each had its own leader and executed missions critical to supporting the overall objective. The implementation of Decentralized Command allowed U.S. forces in Ramadi to provide the most flexible and effective support to the commander's strategic goals of securing the populace, stabilizing the city and ultimately lowering the level of violence in Ramadi.

At first, the SEALs in Task Unit Bruiser expressed skepticism about having to fight alongside Iraqi Soldiers, but Task Unit Bruiser took ownership of the idea and developed powerful relationships with the Iraqi Forces who would eventually take the lead in securing peace in their own country.

U.S. Soldiers, Marines, and SEALs formed a cohesive unit with Iraqi Soldiers, focused exclusively on mission accomplishment. Day after day, section by section, neighborhoods were cleared, and civilians were liberated from the insurgency. In time, the enemy's grip was broken, and a tipping point was reached. The local population recognized that the insurgency was a lost cause and ceased passive support to insurgent fighters and denied them freedom of movement. With the insurgency weakened, the local people organized against the insurgents and launched the Anbar Awakening. Violence plummeted, security and peace were established, and victory in Ramadi was achieved.

With any victory, there is a cost. For us, that cost was heavy. Over 500 U.S. troops were wounded and nearly 100 killed in action, including three Task Unit Bruiser SEALs, Marc Lee, Mike Monsoor, and Ryan Job, as well as a U.S. Marine from ANGLICO SALT 6, Chris Leon. Hundreds more Iraqi Soldiers were killed and wounded. Each and every loss was tragic and devastating. Their sacrifices will never be forgotten.

But the sacrifices were not in vain. Though many had feared Ramadi was unwinnable, the Ready First Brigade's "Seize, Clear, Hold, Build" plan proved successful because the team had the right leaders at every level who relentlessly executed an effective strategy. What had been "all but lost" in 2006, by the following year became the epitome of success. The victory in Ramadi and the Anbar Awakening turned the tide of the war in Anbar Province. Using Ramadi as a blueprint, the same strategy was employed in other troubled areas across Iraq in 2007 and 2008 with similar results.

LEADERSHIP: THE MOST IMPORTANT FACTOR

AS you just read in the synopsis of the Battle of Ramadi, there were a lot of moving pieces. Operations were conducted. Buildings were cleared of enemy fighters. Combat Outposts were built. The city was stabilized and the populace was secured. Additionally, behind all of those front-line tactical efforts, thousands of troops were fed, hundreds of vehicles were fueled and maintained, supplies were delivered, communications were sent, and a multitude of teams and units coordinated their efforts to support one another.

But it is critical to remember that everything that happened during the Battle of Ramadi happened because at some point, somewhere, a leader MADE IT HAPPEN.

It was a leader who came up with the overall strategy. Leaders created operational plans. Leaders conducted missions. Leaders directed troops on the battlefield, and it was leaders who took ownership of their part of the mission and executed it.

When we talk about leaders, we are not only talking about senior leaders. We are not only talking about leaders in charge of 5,000 or 500 people. We are not only talking about leaders who are in charge of 50 people or 5. We are talking about everyone—*everyone* is a leader—even the front-line Soldier, Sailor, Airman, or Marine that takes ownership of their part of the mission and executes. It was leadership at every level that brought victory in the Battle of Ramadi, and it is leadership at every level that brings success to any company or team. So, when we talk about leaders, no matter where you are in the hierarchy of your organization, we are talking about YOU.

Without leadership, nothing happens, and with bad leadership, the wrong things happen. Victory cannot be achieved without leadership, which is why we say leadership is the most important thing on the battlefield, the most important thing in business, and the most important thing in life.

INTRODUCTION: THE BATTLE OF RAMADI

IMPLEMENTATION

1. In Ramadi, U.S. Navy SEALs, Soldiers, Marines, and Iraqi Soldiers worked in close cooperation. In what ways does your team cooperate with other teams to accomplish the mission?

2. In what areas can you improve the cooperation and coordination required for victory? What is your plan for improvement?

3. Describe the areas in your world where you face difficult challenges and winning does not feel possible.

4. How can you attack a difficult problem within the scope of your mission from another angle and develop an innovative solution to achieve a better outcome?

5. How can you apply these lessons directly to your team?

6. How can you apply them to yourself?

IMMEDIATE ACTION DRILL

Write down a specific example of where you were able to overcome a difficult problem with surprising success and what you were able to accomplish. How can you replicate that success in other areas of your life?

NOTES:

PART 1
WINNING THE WAR WITHIN

CHAPTER 1
EXTREME OWNERSHIP

WHAT IS EXTREME OWNERSHIP?

THERE ARE NO EXCUSES

THERE IS NO ONE ELSE TO BLAME

YOU MUST OWN EVERYTHING IN YOUR WORLD; EVERYTHING THAT AFFECTS YOUR MISSION

TAKE OWNERSHIP BOTH UP AND DOWN THE CHAIN OF COMMAND

There are no excuses. There is no one else to blame. On any team, the leader bears total responsibility for the performance of that team. This applies to everyone, no matter where you are in the rank structure of your organization. When we say "leader," we mean leaders at every level, from the most senior leaders at the top of an organization, to mid-level management, to front line leaders—right down to the front line trooper or individual contributor. We're talking to you. YOU OWN IT ALL. Total responsibility, particularly for failures, is a difficult thing to accept.

When things go wrong or something bad happens, it's easy to find someone or something else to blame, such as bad luck, circumstances beyond your control, or the poor performance of others. But when you blame someone or something else, who solves the problems? No one. Therefore, the problems persist, they get worse, and the team's performance suffers. But when you take ownership of problems, examine what more you could have done to improve the situation, and implement a solution going forward, the problems get solved. That is the power of Extreme Ownership.

The best teams are constantly looking to improve performance, add capability, and push the standards even higher. They are never fully satisfied with their performance. It starts with the individual and spreads to each of the team members until a culture of Extreme Ownership becomes the standard.

If your team is delivering substandard performance—if your team is failing to accomplish its mission, whose fault is it? It is your fault. And if you aren't the leader at the top of the chain of command, you can't just blame the boss. No matter where you are in the rank structure of your organization, it's still your fault. You are not following one or more of the Laws of Combat. You are not leading.

You might not have built strong relationships that enable your team to Cover and Move

for each other to ensure the organization wins.

Maybe you have not created Simple plans that everyone on the team understands so they can execute, or asked for clarification to ensure you understand the plan. You haven't communicated effectively in a manner that is simple, clear, and concise.

Perhaps you have not detached from emotion, and taken a step back from the details in order to recognize what is the highest Priority issue you should be focused on and Executed on that task. You haven't allocated the appropriate time and resources to getting the Priority issue solved.

It is possible that you have not properly executed Decentralized Command, ensuring everyone on the team understands the mission, the goal, the end state you are trying to accomplish, and the parameters within which you can make decisions to move the team forward toward that goal. Maybe you haven't developed the people around you to step up and lead, rather than simply waiting for someone else to tell them what to do. Most important, maybe your team doesn't understand ***why*** they are doing what they are doing. Without understanding ***why***, people cannot execute, adapt, or lead effectively.

There are no excuses in Extreme Ownership. You own every problem and you must find a way to win. Extreme Ownership is simple, but it is not easy. It isn't some complex, deep theory learned in a classroom. Extreme Ownership is practical and rooted in common sense, and yet, it is incredibly difficult to implement in real time. When things go wrong, when serious problems arise, when major failures happen, the lure to avoid blame and find an excuse to alleviate yourself from responsibility is powerful. But when you fall prey to this, others do the same and no one owns the problems. Blame is contagious. When everyone in a group simply blames someone else in that group, no one corrects their mistakes, learns from their failures, or makes any adjustments or adaptations. This kind of team never improves. That is why good leaders must do the opposite. To achieve success, you must take Extreme Ownership and build a culture of Extreme Ownership within your team.

WHAT ISN'T EXTREME OWNERSHIP?

Simply saying that something was your fault or apologizing for a mistake is not Extreme Ownership. Words are not magic and they don't make problems go away. As a leader, you have to accept responsibility, genuinely seek a solution, and implement that solution to ensure success. That doesn't mean that you allow your team to sit around and wait for you to solve all the problems. The most successful teams demonstrate a culture of ownership up and down the chain of command, where everyone steps up and works to solve problems, or at least their piece of the overall problem. Such a team will constantly learn, grow, and improve performance. With Extreme Ownership embedded in the culture of your team, you will be unstoppable.

As Echelon Front Instructors, we constantly witness people point out how others need to take Extreme Ownership. Though many don't realize it, by focusing on how Extreme Ownership applies to everyone else, you are blaming them for all the problems. If you find yourself saying, "My boss really needs to hear this," or "I'm doing great but others need to improve" or "Our team is crushing it, but the other teams need a lot of work," then you are demonstrating the opposite of Extreme Ownership. Extreme Ownership isn't about anyone else. EXTREME OWNERSHIP IS ABOUT YOU. Rather than try and force others to change their behavior, focus on the one person you can actually control, which is you.

How do you get others to take ownership? YOU take ownership. They will follow your lead, no matter your rank or title. This is one of the most humbling and difficult concepts to accept. Instead of focusing on all you think is wrong with your team, or your boss, or your mission, or your customer, or someone else, focus on yourself. *Take ownership of everything in your world, everything that impacts your mission: yourself, your actions, your team, and your life.*

HOW TO IMPLEMENT EXTREME OWNERSHIP:

TAKE OWNERSHIP: OWN IT ALL

BE HUMBLE: ADMIT YOUR MISTAKES AND FAILURES, CREATE SOLUTIONS, AND TAKE OWNERSHIP OF IMPLEMENTING THOSE SOLUTIONS.

ANALYZE YOURSELF: EXAMINE WHAT YOU COULD DO BETTER TO ENSURE A SUCCESSFUL OUTCOME

GIVE OWNERSHIP TO SUBORDINATES: ENCOURAGE AND EMPOWER TEAM MEMBERS TO PLAN AND LEAD

LISTEN: EVERYONE CONTRIBUTES TO MISSION ACCOMPLISHMENT

MAKE SURE PEOPLE KNOW WHY THEY ARE DOING WHAT THEY ARE DOING: WITHOUT THE "WHY," THEY CAN'T EXECUTE

TRAIN YOUR TEAM: GIVE THEM THE AUTHORITY AND ABILITY TO ACCOMPLISH THE MISSION

CHAPTER 1: EXTREME OWNERSHIP
IMPLEMENTATION

1. Where in your world do you see opportunities to apply Extreme Ownership?

2. Take a hard look at yourself. Where are you making excuses and why?

3. When you become frustrated with others and find yourself casting blame, how can you take ownership of those situations?

4. Describe a scenario where you can step in and take ownership.

5. Where do you need to detach emotionally from a situation and examine what you can do better to ensure a better outcome?

6. In what ways does your company/organization take ownership? In what ways do they not take ownership?

7. How can you contribute to developing a culture of Extreme Ownership within your team/organization?

IMMEDIATE ACTION DRILL

On what specific task, project, or problem will you take ownership to help your team/organization win and help build a culture of Extreme Ownership within your team/organization?

NOTES:

CHAPTER 2
NO BAD TEAMS, ONLY BAD LEADERS

ONE of the most fundamental and important truths at the heart of Extreme Ownership is the recognition that there are no bad teams, only bad leaders[1]. Leadership is the single greatest factor in any team's performance. Whether a team succeeds or fails is all up to the leader. The leader's attitude sets the tone for the entire team. The leader drives performance—or doesn't. This applies not just to the most senior leader of a team, but to everyone, all the way down to the front line. Anyone on the team can step up and lead, solve problems and collaborate to get the rest of the team moving together in the right direction.

The BUD/S (Basic Underwater Demolition / SEAL training) boat crew example provides a stark illustration of this principle in action. Two Boat Crew teams (2 and 6) competed with the other boat crews to win a series of challenging races. One team, Boat Crew 2, dominated every race. The other team, Boat Crew 6, lost every race and finished significantly behind every other team. We swapped the boat crew leaders—and only the leaders—of Boat Crew 2 and Boat Crew 6. The result? Boat Crew 6, the team that was failing, won the very next race and the next several races. Boat Crew 6 went from the worst team to the best team in the class, illustrating the power of leadership. And Boat Crew 2, the team that had been winning, still performed well, even with a new, underperforming leader. The reason? Because junior members of the team stepped up, filled in the gap and led.

This is only one illustration of many more we witnessed, such as when a platoon commander or a platoon chief was fired due to the SEAL platoon's poor performance. When a new leader was brought in, the same platoon that had failed often turned their performance around and radically improved. We see the same thing occur with frequency in the business world as well.

If your team is underperforming or failing to accomplish your mission, you can't blame the team, the training, the equipment, or the circumstances. Instead, blame yourself. It's not experience or talent that is the greatest driver of success, but leadership. So, recognize that there are no bad teams, only bad leaders. Then, step up, take ownership, build relationships, leverage resources, get problems solved, and lead your team to victory. There's a saying we use at Echelon Front: "It's not what you preach, it's what you tolerate." If you tolerate substandard performance, that's what your team will deliver. If no

---

[1] The phrase comes from "There are no bad teams, only bad officers" philosophy that Colonel David Hackworth learned from his mentors. *About Face* by Colonel David Hackworth, U.S. Army Retired and Julie Sherman.

one is held accountable, that performance becomes the standard. Leaders must enforce high standards across the team, and the toughest but most important place to enforce the standards is in yourself. Set the example for everyone else and that becomes the standard to which others strive.

Leaders should never be satisfied. Constantly strive to improve and build that same mindset into your team and those around you. It starts with a realistic, honest assessment (even brutally honest assessment) of yourself and your team's performance. It continues with every member of the team looking for ways to get better.

The best teams are constantly looking to improve, add capability, and push the standards higher. This attitude starts with the individual and spreads to each of the team members until this becomes the culture, the new standard. The recognition that there are "no bad teams, only bad leaders" comes from taking Extreme Ownership. This mindset enables leaders to build high-performance teams that dominate on any battlefield.

CHAPTER 2: NO BAD TEAMS, ONLY BAD LEADERS

IMPLEMENTATION

1. Which Boat Crew are you in? Why?

2. In what areas are you or your team falling behind?

3. Do you believe you or your team are inclined to point fingers or make excuses? Or does your team take ownership, solve problems, and move forward together? Why?

4. What more can you do to take ownership of problems and get the team united and working together toward the goal?

5. In what areas do you struggle to accept responsibility and own problems that inhibit your team's performance? How can you improve?

6. What are the standards for your team and your organization?

7. Do people within your organization want to be on your team? Why or why not?

IMMEDIATE ACTION DRILL

Write down a specific action you will take to help your team/organization improve and push the standards of performance higher.

NOTES:

CHAPTER 3
BELIEVE

WITHOUT belief in the mission, nothing is possible. A leader needs to believe in the mission in order to convince and inspire others to follow them and accomplish that mission. Leaders must understand and be able to explain how the team's actions are part of something greater than themselves and their own personal interests.

This is not to say that belief in the mission is something that magically makes things happen. While nothing is possible without belief, belief by itself accomplishes nothing. Action must be taken. And that is what belief is: seeing the actual pathway to victory.

It is not always easy to see that pathway and find belief. Leaders must be able to detach from the immediate tactical situation and understand how it fits into the larger strategic goals. Most important, they must understand why they are doing what they are doing. Without the why, it becomes impossible to lead your team when things get difficult. It may be required for leaders to ask questions up the chain of command until they understand the why. If front line leaders and troops understand, they can move forward and make immediate tactical decisions that support the mission.

In Ramadi, our senior leadership required that front line special operations units like Task Unit Bruiser be accompanied by Iraqi Soldiers on every mission. But the battlefield was immensely challenging and dangerous, even with a team we trusted and knew we could rely on. With Iraqi Soldiers alongside us, it made dangerous combat operations all the more difficult. Because of this increased danger, there was push back from our SEALs. The order seemed unreasonable. So, we had to think about it. Why would our chain of command insist we take Iraqi Soldiers with us on every operation? Once we detached and thought through the why, the answer became clear. If Iraqis were never trained and empowered to conduct their own combat missions in Iraq, who was going to do it? Us. Americans. And we would be forced to come back again and again for generations. So, the Iraqis had to learn to provide security for themselves. Once we understood that part of the Ramadi Mission, we were able to communicate it clearly to the rest of our SEALs in Task Unit Bruiser. Their understanding helped them believe in the mission and execute. It's often the case that the front line troops have the least understanding of the strategic goals. It is critical that leaders explain the strategy —the why— all the way down to the front lines. And that front line troops, the individual contributors, and front line leaders ask questions up the chain to clearly understand the why.

But belief alone does not accomplish anything. Your team has to execute. This ties in with the fourth Law of Combat: Decentralized Command. The leader must explain not just what to do, but why. Then they must let their team do the job. A team that believes in the mission and is allowed to execute is a team that wins.

CHAPTER 3: BELIEVE
IMPLEMENTATION

1. What is your mission?

2. What is preventing you or others from fully believing in that mission?

3. What does your pathway to victory actually look like?

4. What questions can you ask your leaders to better understand the why?

5. Where can your team better execute to help accomplish the strategic goal?

6. Are you communicating the why to your subordinates or peers? Have you checked that your team is aligned with strategic goals?

IMMEDIATE ACTION DRILL

Review your answer to question #6. List three specific things you will do to better ensure alignment on the mission, up and down the chain of command.

NOTES:

CHAPTER 4
CHECK THE EGO

OFTEN we get asked: *What is the greatest quality in a leader*? The answer is humility. The biggest killer in combat, in business, and in life is ego. Whether you're leading a SEAL Team engaged in urban warfare, flying a fighter at supersonic speeds, leading teams in a high-pressure industry, or leading your family, ego clouds and disrupts everything. Checking your ego is the key to success. It is simple to say, not easy to do.

WHEN YOU CAN'T KEEP YOUR EGO IN CHECK, YOU:

DON'T LISTEN TO ANYONE

DON'T EVOLVE OR GET BETTER

DON'T ADAPT OR IMPLEMENT NEW TECHNOLOGY AND NEW METHODS

DON'T RESPECT THE COMPETITION

GET COMPLACENT

CAN'T SELF-ASSESS

The U.S. Navy SEAL Teams are one of the most highly screened organizations in the world. We have a 70% attrition rate through our basic training program called BUD/S. But even so, after years of training to make it into the program, and several year's experience in the SEAL Teams, there are still tactical level leaders that get fired.

When a SEAL leader gets fired, it's almost never because they are tactically unsound, physically unfit, unable to read a map or otherwise incompetent. When a SEAL leader gets fired, it is almost always because they lack humility—they can't check their ego. No matter how obvious they're failing or how valid the criticism, they won't listen. They refuse to accept responsibility. They refuse to implement guidance and direction to improve. These leaders are incapable of conducting a realistic, honest self-assessment to examine their own mistakes and failures. They cannot be taught. Therefore, they never improve—their problems persist, often growing, and eventually they get fired. SEAL leaders, regardless of their innate talent or skill, who are willing to listen and show the humility to take ownership of the performance of their team, excel.

The same is true for leaders in every capacity and at every level, in business and in life. Humility is the most important quality in a leader. If you can't keep your ego in check, you set yourself and your team up for failure.

CHAPTER 4: CHECK THE EGO

IMPLEMENTATION

1. What are the “red flags,” or self-indicators, that you use to recognize when your ego is flaring up? Frustration? Anger? Jealousy? When have you noticed them?

2. What are some other people’s red flags or indicators of ego? How do you address these situations?

3. When have you let your ego drive your decisions and cause a problem?

4. How often do you solicit feedback from people on your team or your chain of command? What do you do with that feedback?

5. What are you going to do the next time your ego flares up? List specific actions you will take.

IMMEDIATE ACTION DRILL

Ask a team member or supervisor to provide you with one area of improvement they see a need for, and regardless of what it is, implement it immediately.

NOTES:

PART 2
THE LAWS OF COMBAT

CHAPTER 5: **COVER AND MOVE**

CHAPTER 6: **SIMPLE**

CHAPTER 7: **PRIORITIZE AND EXECUTE**

CHAPTER 8: **DECENTRALIZED COMMAND**

THE LAWS OF COMBAT

LEADERSHIP is the most important thing on the battlefield. While equipment, weaponry, intelligence, tactics, and strategy play a role, leadership is the single greatest factor in determining whether a team succeeds or fails.

When we returned from Ramadi, the most important thing we brought home with us was the leadership lessons that we learned. Our job was to pass those lessons on to the next generation of SEAL leaders. Jocko took command of the West Coast Training Detachment, the command responsible for training all West Coast SEAL Teams preparing to deploy to war zones. The first training exercise Jocko observed was a disaster: The SEAL Platoon leadership had very little control of the situation, elements were not mutually supporting one another, and there was a general sense of chaos throughout the entire training operation. It was clear that the Platoon Leadership did not understand the fundamental principles of combat. Reflecting on the lessons he had learned in his career from other SEAL leaders, lessons that were solidified in the Battle of Ramadi, Jocko distilled the lessons down into the four Laws of Combat:

1. COVER AND MOVE
2. SIMPLE
3. PRIORITIZE AND EXECUTE
4. DECENTRALIZED COMMAND

We began teaching these laws to the young SEAL officers and senior enlisted leaders. The Laws of Combat became the framework for the structured feedback our instructors gave to SEAL platoons going through training. Learning the Laws of Combat came at a heavy cost, paid in the victory of Ramadi. Passing on these lessons learned and Laws of Combat to leaders at all levels is our way to honor those who made the ultimate sacrifice.

With the understanding that leadership is the most important thing on the battlefield, the Laws of Combat answer the fundamental question: ***How do we lead?***

The Laws of Combat are the actions and behaviors employed by the best leaders and the best teams we have observed. Any time a team struggles and falls short in their execution or goals, we can look at the team and observe they are in violation of one or more of the Laws of Combat. The Laws do not stand alone but rather they mutually support one another. All four Laws of Combat are required to operate at the highest level as a leader and a team. Let's break down each Law of Combat.

NOTES:

CHAPTER 5
COVER AND MOVE

COVER and Move is a gunfighting tactic. It's the most fundamental, and perhaps the only true gunfighting tactic that exists. At its core, Cover and Move means every member of a unit works together, mutually supporting one another for the singular purpose of mission accomplishment. In a gunfight, one group provides cover fire to keep the enemy's head down so the other group can advance to a better tactical position. Then, the two groups swap roles, with the group who first moved, now providing cover fire so the first group can move. They continue to leap frog, alternating roles back and forth, covering and moving as they advance toward their goal, eventually pushing through their objective and defeating the enemy. If either group stops covering while the other group is moving in the middle of the fight, the group that is moving is now exposed to enemy fire and might get killed or wounded. This means the mission will likely fail.

This principle also applies to businesses or any organization with different departments and functions all working towards a common goal. The best organizations find ways to work together and support each other. They do not compete against each other or operate independently. If elements of a team forsake this principle and prioritize their success over that of the team, the results can be catastrophic to the team's overall performance.

Within any team, divisions arise. Often, smaller teams within the organization get so focused on their immediate tasks, they forget about what other teams are doing or how these other teams depend on them. These teams may start to compete with one another, and when there are obstacles, animosity and blame develop. This creates unhealthy friction that will degrade performance. It falls on leaders to continually keep the perspective that the strategic mission of the entire organization comes first and foremost.

Despite what is often assumed, the chain of command, or authority granted by the organizational chart, is not the key driver of the Cover and Move principle. In both the military and private sector, relationships are more powerful than the chain of command. ***Relationships are by far the most critical component that enables effective Cover and Move.*** It is vital that you build strong relationships with those you work with and depend on and with those who depend on you. This means you must develop an understanding of the other roles in your organization and build trust between team members. The stronger these relationships are, the more likely you will be able to proactively provide the cover necessary for another team to move, and that they will provide cover for you, so that you can move.

The Cover and Move principle becomes more difficult with scale. Larger organizations typically require additional specialization in functions and roles to deliver their products and services. This specialization creates an undertow that naturally causes teams and departments to drift apart. Leaders at all levels need to actively look for opportunities to break down these barriers and natural silos through supporting other teams with their piece of the mission.

Remember, the enemy is outside the wire. By "wire," we mean the external defensive perimeter around a military forward operating base. The "enemy" is not the other members of your team. Your competition is your real enemy. So, remind yourself and your team that other teammates, departments, customers, and those you depend on to accomplish your mission are all a part of your team. You must develop good, strong, professional relationships with them so you can Cover and Move for each other.

Each member of the team is critical to success, while the main effort and supporting efforts must be clearly defined. If the team fails, everyone fails. Even if a specific member of the team or elements within the team did their job, but the overall mission isn't accomplished, the whole team still fails. Every member of the team must do their part for the overall success of the entire team. If the team wins, everybody wins. Everyone on the team shares in the success. Accomplishing the mission is the highest priority. To understand Cover and Move, is to understand that it's not about you, it's about the mission.

CHAPTER 5: COVER AND MOVE

IMPLEMENTATION

1. Who do you cover for? Inside your team/organization? Outside of your team/organization?

2. Who covers for you? Inside your team/organization? Outside of your team/organization?

3. How can you provide greater support to other team members and other leaders?

4. Where do you need greater support from others?

5. What makes it difficult to work across departments?

6. What makes it difficult to work with other peers, departments, or outside teams/organizations?

IMMEDIATE ACTION DRILL

Who is the one most critical person that you need to improve your professional working relationship with over the next 30 days to help you or your team/organization successfully execute? What steps will you take to improve that relationship?

NOTES:

CHAPTER 6
SIMPLE

COMBAT, like anything in life, has inherent layers of complexity. Simplifying as much as possible is crucial to success. When plans and orders get too complex, people will not understand them. And when things go wrong, which they inevitably will, this lack of understanding can lead to a disastrous outcome. Plans and orders must be simple, clear, and concise.

This principle isn't limited to the battlefield. The business world is also complex. Keeping plans and communications simple is key to the success of any team in combat, business, or life. The best leaders build plans that everyone can understand, all the way down to the lowest level in the organization. The simplest plans are the most genius plans because your individual contributors and front line supervisors can go out and execute them.

Everyone on the team must know and understand their role in the mission and what to do in the event of likely contingencies. If they don't understand, they can't execute. The test for this is binary: Do your people understand or not? How can you determine this? Not by simply asking them. If you ask them if they understand, most will simply say, "Yes." Instead, have them explain their piece of the mission to you. In the military, this is called a "readback." Your team's ability to restate their role and critical tasks will illustrate whether you properly explained it and that they truly understand. As a leader, it doesn't matter how well you think you have presented the information. If your team doesn't understand, you have failed. If you are not in a leadership role, it is still incumbent on you to ask questions and understand the plan so you can execute.

Central to "Simple" is creating a culture within your team where everyone, from the front line troops to mid-level managers and senior leaders, is comfortable asking questions. If you don't fully understand the mission or your role or responsibilities, don't expect the boss to be a mind reader. Take ownership and ask for clarification. Asking for clarity should be encouraged until it is an established aspect of your culture. Effective use of Simple depends on you and your teammates' willingness to raise your hands and ask for more information. With this in mind, when initially laying out a plan, you must formulate it in a way that you can effectively brief (give instructions) so that everyone understands.

When someone doesn't understand the plan or the communications you gave them, there is no possible way they can execute. But don't get frustrated with them. Instead, look at yourself and ensure that you have followed the second law of combat: Simple.

CHAPTER 6: SIMPLE IMPLEMENTATION

1. What is the mission of your organization?

2. How can you ensure that everyone above and below you in your chain of command understands the mission?

3. How do you engage with your leadership to better help you understand the plan?

4. How do you test if your subordinates and peers understand what you are trying to communicate to them?

5. How clear is your communication up and down the chain of command? How do you know?

6. What process is too complex and why? How can you simplify it?

IMMEDIATE ACTION DRILL

Where do you need to simplify your communication to make it more simple, clear and concise? What steps will you take to improve your communication up, down and across the chain of command? In your job and at home?

NOTES:

CHAPTER 7
PRIORITIZE AND EXECUTE

WE have all been in situations where countless things need to be done at once, and we feel overwhelmed. Often these problems compound in a snowball effect where every challenge is complex in its own right, each demanding attention. In combat, even the greatest battlefield leaders cannot solve multiple problems simultaneously. Success begins with determining the highest priority and then executing on that priority.

Leaders must recognize their situation, analyze the numerous problems, decide which problem is the biggest priority, and respond. Their response should focus whatever resources necessary to accomplish the one objective or solve the one problem that will have the biggest impact on the situation. Once the highest priority is handled, move on to the next priority and execute on that. Continue this process until all problems are resolved. If you don't know what to do, you must DETACH.

Unfortunately, this is easier said than done. We are often emotionally tied to the people and problems we encounter. In combat and in any dynamic environment, it is easy to get pulled into a situation where we react with emotion. This is human nature. A leader must make the right decisions without allowing their emotions to control their judgment. In high-stress situations, a leader must detach. Pull yourself back from the chaos and mayhem of the immediate situation and give yourself as much altitude (literal or figurative) to examine the problems. We also must detach from and be in control of our emotions to determine what is best for the greater team and the mission. Doing so will also result in a calming effect on those you are leading through this dynamic situation.

When feeling overwhelmed, even in the most high-pressure situations in combat, we train our SEAL Leaders to:

RELAX. LOOK AROUND. MAKE A CALL.

RELAX Take a breath and calm yourself down. No one makes good decisions when they are spun up or emotional.

LOOK Around. Detach, literally, from the immediate details of the situation. For a combat leader, that means pulling your eye away from your weapon sight, pointing your gun toward the sky and taking a step back to scan the battlefield in front of you in order to evaluate the list of actions that need to happen in order to solve a problem. In business, it is similar: pull yourself out of the weeds or the immediate commotion taking place. Give yourself a little more altitude so you can clearly see what the strategic priorities are. This will enable you to more easily evaluate what is most important.

MAKE a call. Make a decision and disseminate that word to your team. Align your resources to accomplish the most impactful action or priority on the overall situation and most importantly: Execute.

When under pressure, you must be able to "Relax, Look Around, Make a Call" to Prioritize and Execute. But if you have thought through likely contingencies before they arise, it will be far easier for you to Prioritize and Execute once you are in a high-pressure situation. If you've briefed your team (or if you understand the leader's perspective) on what your priorities are during likely contingencies, then the team can Prioritize and Execute in real time without any direct oversight from the leadership. This is the hallmark of the most effective teams, with senior leaders who can think multiple steps ahead to the greater strategic priorities.

Just as in combat, priorities in business and life can rapidly shift. When this happens, ensure that you communicate that change to the rest of the team, both up and down the chain of command. In stressful situations, teams will often get fixated on a single target or priority, even after higher priorities arise. Leaders and team members alike must maintain the ability to quickly re-prioritize efforts and adapt to their constantly changing battlefield or environment.

CHAPTER 7: PRIORITIZE AND EXECUTE
IMPLEMENTATION

1. What are your top priorities?

2. How can you ensure that you are clear on the priorities from your leadership?

3. What are the most common problems you experience? What contingency plans have you developed for them?

4. How often do priorities change? How do you respond?

5. What "Red Flags" or self-indicators of emotional escalation do you have that tell you that it is time to detach?

IMMEDIATE ACTION DRILL

Determine three opportunities, professional or personal, to practice "detaching" this week. Write down what happened, what you did to detach, how the outcome was improved by that detachment, and where you can improve going forward.

NOTES:

CHAPTER 8
DECENTRALIZED COMMAND

EVERYONE LEADS

THE TEAM MUST UNDERSTAND WHAT TO DO AND WHY

DON'T WAIT FOR ORDERS. **LEAD.**

Decentralized Command means everyone leads. The fourth Law of Combat requires leaders at all levels to understand the overall mission (the Commander's Intent) and know they are empowered to make decisions about the key tasks necessary to accomplish that mission. To do this, team members must clearly understand ***why*** they are doing what they are doing.

In order to lead, everyone must understand the mission, the end state, which they are working toward, and the parameters within which they can make decisions and outside of which they cannot. The most important thing for everyone to understand is ***why***, the purpose of their actual task. This is also known as "Commander's Intent"; the underlying goal of the task or mission.

If you find yourself or your people waiting to be told what to do next, then you aren't using proper Decentralized Command. The most effective teams see what needs to be done in order to advance toward the strategic goal and they do it, without needing explicit direction. If someone is asking you to make all decisions for them, don't be the "easy button" and do so. Instead, ask what they think they should do, encourage and empower them to make decisions.

For Decentralized Command to work, even front line employees or individual contributors in charge of no one else but themselves must understand the overall mission. Everyone is expected to step up and lead, find solutions to their problems, and seek new opportunities on which to capitalize. The employee actually in the situation is closest to the problem and has the most context on what's required to fix it, which puts them in the best position to solve it. Understanding the ***why*** behind what you are doing allows you to lead and solve problems without waiting for orders. If you are in charge of a team, make sure you think through the ***why*** and explain it to your team. If you aren't in charge but don't understand the ***why***, make sure you ask for clarification. Either way, it's your responsibility to know so you can lead.

Effective use of Decentralized Command requires the leader to outline the parameters for their team members. Team members must fully understand what is within their decision-making authority—the "left and right limits" of their responsibility. It's also incumbent on team members to ask their boss for clarification if they aren't clear. This clarity will help team members execute with confidence and be more decisive with their actions. Additionally, team members need to push information and decisions outside of their authority up to senior leaders so they can take appropriate actions. But the best leaders, rather than asking, "What do you want me to do?" make recommendations up the chain of command with a solution of how to solve the problem.

CHAPTER 8: DECENTRALIZED COMMAND

IMPLEMENTATION

1. Explain the why behind your mission or key task. Does everyone on your team understand the why? How can you help explain it to them?

2. Do people on your team take projects/tasks and run with them or do they wait for specific direction from leadership on what to do? Why do they do that?

3. Do you understand the parameters within which you can make decisions and outside of which, you cannot make decisions without approval? If you do, how can you increase your knowledge and confidence of these parameters? If you do not, what can you do to get clarification and better understand these parameters?

4. In what areas are you being the "easy button" for your team or your peers by making the decisions or solving problems for other people rather than teaching/training them to act themselves?

5. How do you prepare your subordinates or junior personnel to lead? If you are an individual contributor, how do you prepare yourself to lead?

6. What indicators suggest you've become too "decentralized"?

7. Are you being micromanaged? Why? What can you do to build trust with your leadership?

8. Are you micromanaging? Why? What can you do to improve your trust in your team?

IMMEDIATE ACTION DRILL

Go to your junior leaders or team members and ask them what they think the best solution would be to solve a particular problem or obstacle that your team is facing. If the solution makes sense, let them run with it. If their solution needs some adjustment to meet time or resource constraints, ask earnest questions to better understand their perspective and ensure they have thought through all the adjustments you are concerned about. If their solution simply isn't feasible, explain why and encourage them to keep developing solutions to problems/obstacles.

NOTES:

PART III
SUSTAINING VICTORY

CHAPTER 9
PLAN

GOOD planning is crucial to the success of any operation, project or task. Leaders must understand the mission. They also need to ensure their people understand the mission as well. What we call "Commander's Intent" in the military is really just the strategic purpose behind the tactical operation—another term for understanding the ***why*** behind a mission tasking. Understanding the Commander's Intent is what allows subordinate leaders and front-line troops to develop effective plans and make good decisions on the ground in real time. If you're a front line trooper, ensure you understand your commander's intent. If you don't, ask.

When building a plan, leaders should delegate as much as possible of the planning process down to subordinate leaders and their teams. Giving front line troops ownership of the plan helps them understand the reasons behind the plan, and reinforces their belief in the mission. This translates to effective execution on the ground. How do you create "buy in" on the team for your plan? Give ownership. It's better to go with a team member's plan who has a 70 percent solution over your own plan that is a 90 percent solution. Why? Because when someone develops and owns the plan, they will usually figure out a way to work through problems and obstacles to succeed. When you impose a plan on your team, dictate every aspect, and mandate that they follow your plan, the opposite is true: the team looks at you to solve all the problems. Delegating the planning not only gives the team ownership of the plan, it also allows your team members an opportunity to grow as leaders and learn along the way. If you are a junior member of the team, seek every opportunity to step up and take charge of some aspect of the plan.

Senior leaders need to supervise the overall planning process and not get bogged down in the details. Give your key leaders the strategic goals, your commander's intent, some parameters within which they need to work, and let them plan their piece of the mission. The goal is for the senior leader to ensure strategic objectives are met and to "stand back and be the tactical genius"—identify weaknesses or holes in the plan that those immersed in the details might have missed.

During the briefing phase, leaders need to help prioritize the information, so it is presented in a simple, clear, and concise format. The planning and briefing process must encourage discussion, questions, and clarification from everyone involved. Leaders should encourage interaction and ensure their teams understand the plan.

THE TEST FOR A SUCCESSFUL BRIEF IS SIMPLE:
DO THE TEAM AND SUPPORTING ELEMENTS UNDERSTAND IT?

The plan must mitigate risks, but there are some risks that cannot be mitigated, and leaders should focus on those risks that can be controlled. Leaders must be comfortable accepting some level of risk, or, as John Paul Jones, said, "Those who will not risk cannot win."

After executing the plan it's important to bring the team together for a debrief and cover everything that could be improved upon. In order to do this, the leader must carve out time into the schedule. This is a time to be brutally honest with yourself and analyze what you can do and what the team can do to improve performance on the next operation.

A LEADER'S CHECKLIST FOR PLANNING SHOULD INCLUDE THE FOLLOWING:

ANALYZE the Mission. Understand higher headquarters' mission, Commander's Intent, and end state (the goal). Identify and state your own Commander's Intent and end state for the specific mission.

IDENTIFY personnel, assets, resources, and time available.

DECENTRALIZE the planning process. Empower key leaders within the team to analyze possible courses of action.

DETERMINE a specific course of action. Lean toward selecting the simplest course of action. Focus efforts on the best course of action (if multiple options).

EMPOWER key leaders to develop the plan for the selected course of action.

PLAN for likely contingencies through each phase of the operation.

MITIGATE risks that can be controlled.

DELEGATE portions of the plan and brief to key junior leaders. Stand back and be the tactical genius.

EVALUATE, check, and continuously question the plan against emerging information to ensure it still fits the situation.

BRIEF the plan to all participants and supporting assets. Emphasize Commander's Intent. Ask questions and engage in discussion and interaction with the team to ensure they understand.

CONDUCT post-operational debrief after execution. Analyze lessons learned and implement them in future planning.

PLANNING CHECKLIST

- [x] DOES EVERYONE INVOLVED UNDERSTAND THE COMMANDER'S INTENT? THIS WILL HELP THEM MAKE DECISIONS THAT SUPPORT THE LONG-TERM STRATEGY.

- [x] ARE THE FRONT-LINE EMPLOYEES IN CHARGE OR ASSISTING WITH DEVELOPING THE PLAN (IS PLANNING DECENTRALIZED)? DO THESE PEOPLE HAVE THE RESOURCES THAT THEY NEED TO SUCCEED?

- [x] DO THE PEOPLE EXECUTING HAVE OWNERSHIP OF THE PLAN? REMEMBER GIVING THEM OWNERSHIP WILL DRIVE THEM TO SOLVE PROBLEMS THAT COME UP AND ENSURE SUCCESS.

- [x] ARE SENIOR LEADERS FOCUSED ON STRATEGIC OBJECTIVES RATHER THAN GETTING BOGGED DOWN IN THE DETAILS? ARE LEADERS ACTING AS "TACTICAL GENIUSES" IN ORDER TO IMPROVE PLANS?

- [x] IS THE PLAN SIMPLE? IS THE PLAN BEING COMMUNICATED IN A SIMPLE WAY? DOES EVERYONE INVOLVED UNDERSTAND THE PLAN SO THEY CAN EXECUTE?

- [x] DOES THE PLAN MITIGATE RISK AND INCLUDE CONTINGENCIES FOR WHEN THINGS INEVITABLY CHANGE?

- [x] IS THERE A DEBRIEF PROCESS IN PLACE TO LEARN AFTER EXECUTING THE PLAN?

CHAPTER 9: PLAN IMPLEMENTATION

1. Do you understand the "commander's intent," or the purpose, end state and goal of the mission you are trying to achieve? If you do, how can you help others better understand? If you do not, what will you do to get clarification?

2. Does your team, your peers, or the people you depend on to support you understand your "commander's intent," or the purpose, end state and goal of the mission you are trying to achieve? How can you test their knowledge and better ensure they understand?

3. What can you do to more effectively detach from the details and stay focused on the strategic goals?

4. How do you encourage questions and discussion among your team to ensure that everyone fully understands the plan, the mission, and the key tasks they must accomplish?

5. If you are leading a team, to whom on your team can you give ownership of planning pieces of the mission? If you are a junior leader or individual contributor, what supporting plans can you take ownership of to better support your leaders?

6. If you were tasked to brief your piece of the mission, what is your game plan to deliver an exceptional brief to your team and how will you do it?

IMMEDIATE ACTION DRILL

Identify three likely contingencies that you and your team should be prepared for and create a plan ready to implement should those contingencies occur. Encourage others on your team to do the same.

NOTES:

CHAPTER 10
LEADING UP AND DOWN THE CHAIN OF COMMAND

ONE of the most important jobs of any leader is to support your immediate leadership. The senior leaders of a team must always present a united front to the team. A public display of discontent or disagreement with the chain of command undermines the authority of leaders at all levels, including yours. This can be catastrophic to the performance of any organization.

ENGAGE YOUR LEADERSHIP DIRECTLY

UNDERSTAND THEIR PRIORITIES AND EXPECTATIONS

PROVIDE SOLUTIONS AND ENSURE YOUR LEADERSHIP SUCCEEDS

BUILD STRONG RELATIONSHIPS AT EVERY LEVEL BOTH UP AND DOWN THE CHAIN OF COMMAND

BRIEF YOUR TEAM ON ALL FACETS OF THE MISSION

HOLD YOURSELF RESPONSIBLE FOR EVERYTHING

Any good leader is immersed in the broad spectrum of planning and execution of his or her team. Those leaders possess detailed knowledge of the bigger picture and the specific tasks to be accomplished. This information does not automatically translate to direct reports (in military terms, subordinates) within the team. Members of the team - the tactical level operators - are rightly focused on their jobs and must be to accomplish the mission. They do not need the full knowledge and insight of the senior leaders. Nor do the senior leaders need the intricate details of the tactical level operators' jobs. But each must have an understanding of the other's role. It is critical that you routinely and effectively communicate with your team members to help them understand their role in the overall mission. You must connect the dots between the day-to-day operations of the team and the impact they have on the larger, strategic goals of the organization. You must also help your team members prioritize their efforts in a rapidly changing, dynamic environment. That is leading down the chain of command. It requires regularly stepping out of your office or workspace, and personally engaging with your front line troops or individual contributors, understanding their particular challenges, and reading them into the bigger picture.

There is an equally important form of leadership we call leading up the chain of command. This entails building relationships with your leaders so you can engage directly with them in order to obtain the decisions and support necessary to enable your team to accomplish its mission and ultimately win. A leader must deliver the most critical information necessary so that his or her boss can make decisions promptly and enable the boss to allocate the support necessary to accomplish the team's mission.

If your boss isn't making timely decisions or providing the necessary support for you and your team, don't blame the boss. The boss doesn't want you to fail. Instead, blame yourself. You must take ownership and do more to educate, influence, and inform your boss to make those decisions correctly and timely. You must build a better relationship with your boss so that the boss actually trusts you and listens to you. Instead of blaming your boss, take Extreme Ownership. Examine what you can do to better convey the critical information necessary for decisions to be made and get the resources and support you need to be successful, and do it.

Leading up the chain takes much more savvy and skill than leading down the chain. When leading up the chain, you cannot fall back on your rank or positional authority (which you shouldn't do anyway). Instead, you must use experience, knowledge, communication, and relationships to influence your senior leaders.

When you understand the strategic picture and how your team can best contribute to victory, you can plant an idea in the mind of your boss or your senior leadership, and nurture that idea until they decide to execute it as if it were their own. It doesn't matter who gets the credit. All that matters is that the team wins. When the team wins, everyone wins. That is the greatest possible outcome.

CHAPTER 10: LEADING UP AND DOWN THE CHAIN

IMPLEMENTATION

1. Where can you provide greater support to your leadership?

2. What can you start doing to build a better relationship with your boss? With your team?

3. How do you handle a situation when you or your team need to execute a plan or action that you don't agree with?

4. How can you best capture the impact that your team has on the overall strategic mission and brief them on what they have accomplished?

5. What steps can you take to find a way to better understand how your immediate tactical plan contributes to the greater strategic plan?

IMMEDIATE ACTION DRILL

Determine one area where you will push more information up the chain of command to give your leadership the information they need to vector resources, prioritize efforts and make strategic decisions. Determine one area where you will push more information down the chain of command to ensure your team fully understands how what they do impacts the success of the overall team and the greater strategic mission.

NOTES:

CHAPTER 11
DECISIVENESS AMID UNCERTAINTY

LEADERS will always be faced with uncertainty. The picture is never complete. On the battlefield, as in every arena of business and life, there is always an element of unknown. As a leader, you must be comfortable with this. You have to make decisions, then be ready to adjust those decisions quickly based on evolving situations and new information. Don't allow yourself to be paralyzed by fear or indecision, which results in inaction. It is critical for leaders to act decisively amid uncertainty; to make the best decisions they can based off the immediate information available.

Waiting for the 100 percent right solution leads to delay, indecision, and an inability to execute. Be prepared to make an educated decision based off your previous experiences, knowledge, training, and education. Calculate the likely outcomes and take into consideration all the information available to you. One of the best ways to do this is through small, iterative steps in the direction you think is best. Without the complete picture, only move as far as needed to evaluate, reassess, make corrections, and move again. This enables rapid, incremental decisions. You can always adjust as new information emerges. Such a series of these small, iterative decisions collectively will move the team in the direction you need to go. It enables you to be decisive amid uncertainty.

The incident where one of our SEAL snipers spotted an unidentified man with a "scoped weapon" provided a sobering example of the need to be decisive amid uncertainty. The picture was not clear and the results could have been catastrophic. Despite the pressure to make a decision in line with the prevailing suspicion of what was happening, Leif needed more information. Instead of ordering a shot to be taken by his sniper Leif requested an incremental step—for a team to be sent into that building to judge the reaction of the unidentified man. As it turned out, the unidentified man was an American Soldier. Leif held the line, and thank God that he did in that scenario.

Even when the picture isn't complete, you have to make a decision to move the team forward toward the goal, in the manner you think best, based on whatever information is currently available.

On the battlefield, we say, "The enemy gets a vote." That means you can't control what the enemy does. In the civilian world, you can't control what your competition does. You often cannot control market conditions or consumer trends. But you still need to be comfortable making decisions based on the information you have available. There is no 100% right solution. There will always be some element of risk. But as a leader, no matter where you fall in your team's organizational chart, you have to be decisive amid uncertainty.

CHAPTER 11: DECISIVENESS AMID UNCERTAINTY

IMPLEMENTATION

1. Do you delay decisions that should be easy to make out of fear of being fired or reprimanded? Why do you think that will happen?

2. Reflect on one hard decision you made where you had to make quick adjustments due to new information coming in. What was the outcome?

3. What would have happened if you did not make quick adjustments with your decision?

4. In what areas are your competitors decisively maneuvering to give them a greater advantage over you? What small, incremental steps can you take to counter them?

5. In what areas are you hesitant to take action and so you need to be more Default: Aggressive toward solving a problem or seizing the initiative? In what areas are you being too aggressive and you need to detach, properly evaluate the situation and implement steps to mitigate the risks that you can control?

IMMEDIATE ACTION DRILL

Where can you take a small, iterative step to move yourself or your team in the direction you think is best based off the information currently available? What will be your indicators to guide decisions on follow-on small, iterative steps?

NOTES:

CHAPTER 12
DISCIPLINE EQUALS FREEDOM: THE DICHOTOMY OF LEADERSHIP

EVERYONE wants freedom. It is the ultimate goal. That is what we live and work for and what many veterans have fought and died for; to live in a country where we have freedom.

We want physical freedom; the ability to run, jump, swim, hike, bike, climb. How do we earn this freedom? We need to consistently eat right, train hard, stretch and get enough rest. We need to be disciplined with our bodies.

We want financial freedom. How do we earn this freedom? We need to save money, invest well, stick to a budget, and not waste money on things we don't need. We need financial discipline.

Everyone wants more free time. How do we get more free time? We need to get up early, create and stick to a disciplined time management schedule, and not waste time. We need to be disciplined with our time to give us more free time to do whatever we want.

It is through discipline we get the freedoms we want: Discipline Equals Freedom.

Discipline and freedom are opposing forces. Discipline is rigid, structured, and controlled. Freedom is the opposite: unconfined and unrestrained. When we think of freedom, we think of doing whatever we want, whenever we want. And of course, that is what we desire: freedom. But, if we look closer, we discover that while discipline and freedom are opposing forces, they are closely related. In fact, the pathway to freedom is through discipline; we need discipline to achieve freedom. However, it is also a dichotomy that must be balanced. Excessive discipline can stifle personal and team development and undermine free thinking. Contrarily, without enough discipline the team will not know what to do in critical situations or how to respond to crisis. When we strike the right balance, a disciplined team will have structured plans and standard operating procedures in place that allow for rapid and unified execution, but still enough freedom to adjust, adapt, and maneuver to emerging changes and contingencies. That balance is dynamic, changing constantly with every person and every team, and as a leader, you must find the balance between discipline and freedom.

Discipline Equals Freedom is a powerful tool for both personal and team development. This simple equation transfers into all aspects of business and life.

If you want to be able to act decisively, you must have the discipline to train and increase your knowledge and skill set. If you want to maintain a better safety record, you must impose disciplined rules and strict accountability to ensure safety. If you want to be more efficient, you must establish disciplined standard operating procedures that ensure the most effective processes and methods are utilized to execute.

Standard Operating Procedures (SOPs) are generated by teams and organizations to ensure the most effective and safest techniques are employed to complete repetitive simple and complex tasks. There's an adage in the military that SOPs are written in blood. They come from the costly lessons learned in an unforgiving environment, and they must be utilized by everyone to prevent those same mistakes from being repeated. The same is true in business. SOPs should be written down and taught from day one to everyone on your team. This will create uniformity and ensure everyone understands the origins and reasons behind why they are doing their jobs a certain way. It is this understanding that allows for freedom—deviations, flexibility, and changes when problems arise. Remember, even the best SOPs don't work 100% of the time, and SOPs don't relieve you of the requirement to think about every situation. Leaders need to think, all the time.

In the SEAL Teams, we had SOPs for everything we did, such as the gear we wore, how we lined up in patrol formation, how we breached a door, how we loaded and unloaded from vehicles. Most think this seemingly unending list of SOPs would restrict us in combat and make us rigid and inflexible. But the reality is, they set us free. Combat is a dynamic environment, and units that move freely and aggressively have the advantage. Our SOPs provided us the discipline to be agile and flexible in combat. If a Platoon Commander wanted one of his squads to take down a building that we hadn't planned for, it would be a simple command: "Squad 2, take that building." The Platoon Commander wouldn't have to spend a lengthy brief with the Squad Leader discussing who was going, what they were going to do, and how they were going to do it because they had built SOPs around all of those things. Different platoons use the same SOPs so they can combine elements from different platoons and seamlessly execute. SEAL Platoons are extraordinarily agile because of the adherence to SOPs and relentless training to them.

The Dichotomy of Leadership is not only about discipline and freedom. There are an infinite number of dichotomies that a leader must balance. A leader must communicate—but not too much. A leader must plan—but not get stuck in a planning cycle that never ends. A leader must be aggressive and make things happen—but must not be overly aggressive and take unreasonable risk. A leader must be willing and able to step up and lead—but a leader must also know when to follow someone else's lead.

The list of dichotomies goes on forever. And in the end, the good leader balances these dichotomies. Extreme behavior or extreme reactions as a leader almost always create a negative impact. Don't be extreme—be balanced.

CHAPTER 12: DISCIPLINE EQUALS FREEDOM

IMPLEMENTATION

1. Where do you see room for increased discipline? By applying that discipline, what freedom will be possible?

____

____

____

____

____

____

2. Where do you see room for better process or SOPs (Standard Operating Procedures)? Whose job is it to develop SOPs?

____

____

____

____

____

____

3. Why do we need to impose more disciplined practices?

____

____

____

____

____

____

____

4. Where do you see too much discipline or restriction? Why is it there? What can you do to fix it?

5. Are there any other traits you or your organization have that tend to be extreme? Is there anywhere you can be more balanced?

IMMEDIATE ACTION DRILL

Review your answer to question #1 and write down and execute on three things that you can do in the next 30 days to implement greater discipline that will enable more freedom in your life.

IMMEDIATE ACTION DRILL

Conduct an honest, realistic self-assessment of your leadership performance. Complete the Echelon Front Balance Assessment Exercise, identify one (1) area that is out of balance that you need to fix, and write down what specific steps you will take to fix it.

Access Balance Assessment form: *https://echelonfront.com/balance-assessment/*

NOTES:

NOTES

APPENDIX//
GLOSSARY OF TERMS

GLOSSARY OF TERMS

AFTER ACTION REVIEW (AAR) Structured debrief of what happened, why it happened, and what could be done better as well as any other takeaways.

COMMANDER'S INTENT The strategic goal of the mission or task. It is the explanation of not what to do but why which enables leaders at every level of the team to step up and lead with Decentralized Command.

COVER AND MOVE Teamwork. The team must work together, mutually supporting one another in order to accomplish the goal. If the team succeeds, everyone succeeds. If the team fails, everyone fails. Accomplishing the mission is the highest priority.

DECENTRALIZED COMMAND Everyone leads. To enable this, leaders at all levels must understand the mission and the why behind the mission. They must also understand the end-state, the goal, and the parameters within which they can operate.

DICHOTOMY OF LEADERSHIP Leaders must strive to find the right balance to be effective when two opposing forces are pulling them in different directions, and they both are correct. Everyone is different, and everything is dynamic. Work to achieve balance every day.

DISCIPLINE EQUALS FREEDOM There is no hack. There are no secrets, no shortcuts, no tricks. The pathway to freedom is through discipline.

EXECUTION CHECK LIST (EX CHECK) List of key tasks to complete and timelines or dates for their completion.

EXTREME OWNERSHIP The mindset and attitude which is foundational to the best leaders and organizations: they don't make excuses, blame others or circumstances. Instead, they take ownership of mistakes and failures and implement effective solutions that get problems solved.

LEADER To be a leader means to get a group of people to effectively execute a complex mission to accomplish strategic goals in a dynamic environment.

It is directly applicable from combat leadership to leadership in the business world and life. The principles are immediately transferable to what you do, every day, in every aspect of your world.

LEADERSHIP The most important thing on the battlefield and to the success of any organization in any situation. It is the critical difference between success and failure, winning and losing.

PRIORITIZE AND EXECUTE You can't do everything at once. If you try, you will fail. Even if everything appears to be a priority, you still need to detach, figure out the highest priority task, and then execute to accomplish it. When things feel overwhelming, detach from emotion. Relax. Look Around. Make a Call.

READ BACK A tool to ensure communication is simple and understood by the team. Ask a team member to explain your communication back to you in their words, if they explained it correctly, you communicated effectively. If not, you have failed to communicate effectively and must explain again. Remember to take ownership of both the readback and the outcome.

SIMPLE Plans, orders and communication must be simple, clear, and concise so that everyone understands. If your team does not understand, they can't execute.

SUBORDINATE A junior member of the team in the rank structure of the organization. It is standard military term and does not denote any inferiority but merely refers to organizational hierarchy.

STANDARD OPERATING PROCEDURES (SOPs) Set of detailed instructions for completing a certain recurring task; best practice. Should be developed by the person/people completing the task and reviewed regularly for improvements.

THERE ARE NO BAD TEAMS, ONLY BAD LEADERS
An important truth that leaders must accept in order to succeed. The only metric that matters is whether you were effective or ineffective in accomplishing your mission. As a leader, no matter your rank or title, you are responsible for the success or failure of your team. Step up and Lead.

IT IS ALL ON YOU, BUT NOT ABOUT YOU.

EXCERPT FROM LEADERSHIP STRATEGY AND TACTICS: FIELD MANUAL BY JOCKO WILLINK

AS a leader, there are no excuses and there is no one else to blame. You have to make decisions. You have to build relationships. You have to communicate so that everyone can understand. You have to control your ego and your emotions. You have to be able to detach. You need to instill pride in the team. You need to train the team. You need to be balanced and tactful and aware and you have to take ownership. The list goes on and on and makes up this incredibly complex undertaking that we call leadership. And if you do all those things well—if you lead effectively—the team will be successful and the mission will be accomplished. If you do not lead effectively, you will fail and the team will not accomplish the mission.

LEADERSHIP IS ALL ON YOU.

But, at the same time, leadership is not about you. Not at all. Leadership is about the team. The team is more important than you. The moment you put your own interests above the team and above the mission, is the moment you fail as a leader. When you think you can get away with it—when you think the team won't notice your self-serving maneuvers—you are wrong. They will see it and they will know it.

The leadership strategies and tactics in this book are to be used not so you can be successful. These strategies and tactics are to be used so the team can be successful. If you use them to further your own career or your own agenda, eventually, these strategies and tactics will backfire and bring you down. You will fail as a leader and as a person.

But if you use these strategies and tactics with the goal of helping others and of helping the team accomplish its mission, then the team will succeed. And if the team succeeds, you will win as a leader and as a person. But infinitely more important: your people will win. And that is true leadership.

EVERY CHALLENGE A COMPANY OR ORGANIZATION MAY FACE:

LEADERSHIP IS THE SOLUTION.

OUR MISSION

Echelon Front's mission is to educate, train, mentor, and inspire LEADERS and organizations to overcome challenges, seize opportunities, and achieve total victory. Utilizing lessons learned and proven in combat, we help LEADERS develop the core ACTIONS and MINDSETS necessary to tackle issues including strategy, execution, safety and risk mitigation, mission planning, innovation, team building, and crisis management strategies, and cultural transformation.

OUR SERVICES

Echelon Front offers practical, experience-based solutions to complex problems based on leadership lessons learned in the military and the private sector. Using our vast experience with dynamic leadership challenges, we connect those lessons to both business and life so our clients can apply them immediately. We don't teach theory learned in a classroom. We offer a wide range of unique, customized, and personalized services designed to get your team executing at the highest level possible.

LEADERSHIP CONSULTING

LEADERSHIP DEVELOPMENT AND ALIGNMENT PROGRAMS (LDAP)
ASSESSMENTS AND STRATEGIC ADVISING

IN-PERSON TRAINING

ON-SITE TRAINING – HALF-DAY, FULL-DAY AND MULTI-DAY WORKSHOPS
KEYNOTE PRESENTATIONS

VIRTUAL TRAINING

VIRTUAL TRAINING AND CERTIFICATION PROGRAMS - EXTREME OWNERSHIP ACADEMY
WEBINARS AND VIRTUAL WORKSHOPS
VIRTUAL KEYNOTE PRESENTATIONS

EXPERIENTIAL TRAINING

EXTREME OWNERSHIP FIELD TRAINING EXERCISES (FTX)
BATTLEFIELD REVIEW
EXTREME OWNERSHIP MUSTER CONFERENCE

ECHELONFRONT.COM

THE EXTREME OWNERSHIP ACADEMY IS OUR VIRTUAL LEADERSHIP TRAINING PLATFORM WHERE WE APPLY AND INSTILL THE PRINCIPLES OF EXTREME OWNERSHIP AND THE LAWS OF COMBAT THROUGH SUSTAINED ONLINE LEARNING AND DIRECT LIVE INTERACTION.

ON DEMAND LEADERSHIP TRAINING FOR YOU AND YOUR TEAM

START BY CREATING A FREE ACCOUNT AND GET INSTANT ACCESS TO THESE COURSES:

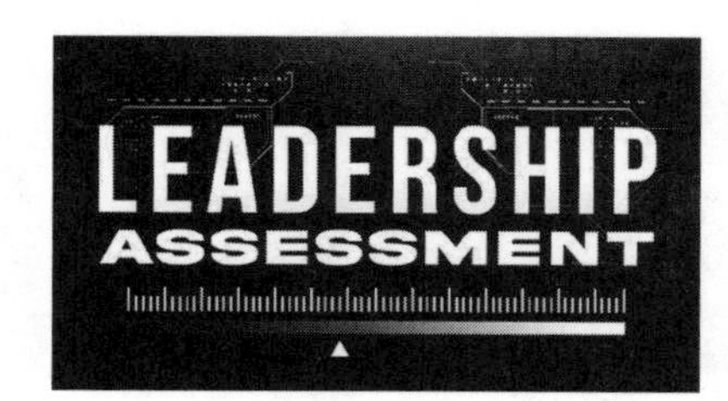

THE LEADERSHIP ASSESSMENT TEST WILL SHOW YOU WHERE YOU ARE ON YOUR LEADERSHIP JOURNEY AND, MORE IMPORTANTLY, WHERE YOUR LEADERSHIP SKILLS NEED IMPROVEMENT.

THE BARRIERS TO EXTREME OWNERSHIP COURSE, WITH JAMIE COCHRAN AND JOCKO, EXPLORES THE BARRIERS THAT HOLD US BACK FROM TAKING OWNERSHIP, AND HOW WE CAN OVERCOME THEM.

THE EXTREME OWNERSHIP FRAMEWORK COURSE, WITH DAVE BERKE AND JOCKO, TEACHES THE 5 STEPS TO TAKING EFFECTIVE OWNERSHIP IN DIFFICULT SITUATIONS AND WHEN HAVING HARD CONVERSATIONS.

CREATE A FREE ACCOUNT AT ACADEMY.ECHELONFRONT.COM

ONCE YOU COMPLETE THE FREE TRAINING EXPLORE OUR FOUNDATIONS AND STRATEGY AND TACTICS COURSES THAT ARE AVAILABLE FOR PURCHASE ON THE ACADEMY. YOU CAN ALSO JOIN OUR LIVE SESSIONS TO SOLVE YOUR INDIVIDUAL LEADERSHIP CHALLENGES.

ACCESS 30+ HOURS OF ONLINE COURSE MATERIAL THAT EACH INCLUDE:

- A COMBAT EXAMPLE FROM THE BATTLEFIELD
- OUTLINE OF THE LEADERSHIP PRINCIPLE
- APPLICATION TO BUSINESS OR INDUSTRY
- APPLICATION EXERCISES
- FINAL LEARNING CHECK

EXTREME OWNERSHIP ACADEMY LIVE SESSIONS

INTERACT DIRECTLY WITH JOCKO, LEIF, AND THE REST OF THE ECHELON FRONT LEADERSHIP INSTRUCTORS ONCE A WEEK TO DISCUSS AND SOLVE YOUR SPECIFIC LEADERSHIP CHALLENGES.

SAVE 20% WITH CODE: AMAZON20

OR SIMPLY SCAN THE QR CODE TO GET STARTED AT ACADEMY.ECHELONFRONT.COM

RECOMMENDED READING FOR THOSE THAT ARE LOOKING TO GET AFTER IT

READ. LEAD. WIN.

EXTREME OWNERSHIP

THE DICHOTOMY OF LEADERSHIP

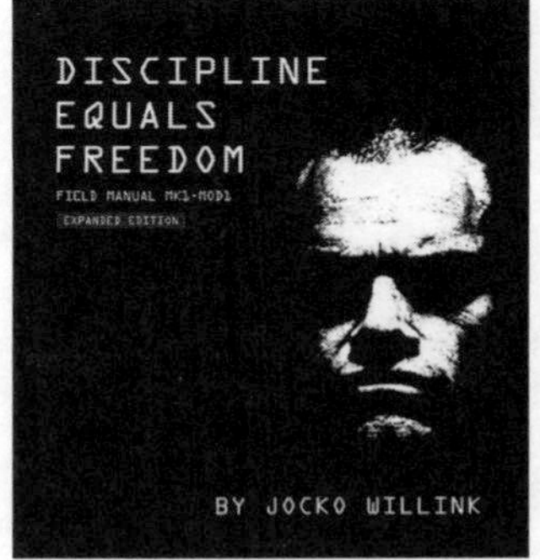

Discipline Equals Freedom

Leadership Strategy and Tactics

The Code. The Evaluation. The Protocols.

STRONGER KIDS FOR A STRONGER TOMORROW

Way of the Warrior Kid 1

Way of the Warrior Kid 2

Way of the Warrior Kid 3

Way of the Warrior Kid 4

Way of the Warrior Kid 5

Way of the Warrior Kid Coloring

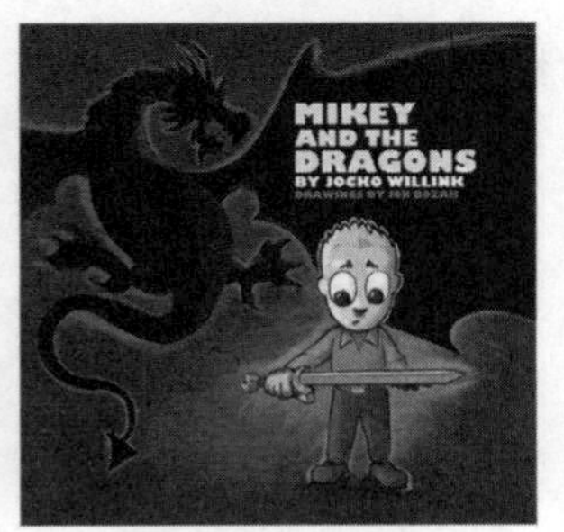

Mikey and the Dragons